BON J_____H

CW00419338

B
EDITION

WISE PUBLICATIONS
LONDON/NEW YORK/SYDNEY/PARIS/COPENHAGEN/MADRID/TOKYO

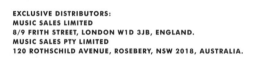

EXCLUSIVE DISTRIBUTORS:
MUSIC SALES LIMITED
8/9 FRITH STREET, LONDON W1D 3JB, ENGLAND.
MUSIC SALES PTY LIMITED
120 ROTHSCHILD AVENUE, ROSEBERY, NSW 2018, AUSTRALIA.

ORDER NO.AM967230
ISBN 0-7119-8479-4
THIS BOOK © COPYRIGHT 2000 BY WISE PUBLICATIONS.

MUSIC ARRANGED BY MATT COWE.
MUSIC ENGRAVED BY PAUL EWERS MUSIC DESIGN.
ARTWORK COUTESY OF WARNER BROS. PUBLICATIONS.

PRINTED IN THE UNITED KINGDOM BY CALIGRAVING LIMITED, THETFORD, NORFOLK.

YOUR GUARANTEE OF QUALITY:

AS PUBLISHERS, WE STRIVE TO PRODUCE EVERY BOOK TO
THE HIGHEST COMMERCIAL STANDARDS.

THE MUSIC HAS BEEN FRESHLY ENGRAVED AND, WHILST ENDEAVOURING
TO RETAIN THE ORIGINAL RUNNING ORDER OF THE RECORDED ALBUM,
THE BOOK HAS BEEN CAREFULLY DESIGNED TO MINIMISE AWKWARD PAGE TURNS
AND TO MAKE PLAYING FROM IT A REAL PLEASURE.

PARTICULAR CARE HAS BEEN GIVEN TO SPECIFYING ACID-FREE, NEUTRAL-SIZED
PAPER MADE FROM PULPS WHICH HAVE NOT BEEN ELEMENTAL CHLORINE BLEACHED.

THIS PULP IS FROM FARMED SUSTAINABLE FORESTS AND WAS PRODUCED WITH
SPECIAL REGARD FOR THE ENVIRONMENT. THROUGHOUT, THE PRINTING AND BINDING
HAVE BEEN PLANNED TO ENSURE A STURDY, ATTRACTIVE PUBLICATION WHICH
SHOULD GIVE YEARS OF ENJOYMENT.

IF YOUR COPY FAILS TO MEET OUR HIGH STANDARDS, PLEASE INFORM US
AND WE WILL GLADLY REPLACE IT.

MUSIC SALES' COMPLETE CATALOGUE DESCRIBES THOUSANDS OF TITLES AND
IS AVAILABLE IN FULL COLOUR SECTIONS BY SUBJECT, DIRECT FROM MUSIC SALES LIMITED.
PLEASE STATE YOUR AREAS OF INTEREST AND SEND A CHEQUE/POSTAL ORDER FOR £1.50 FOR
POSTAGE TO: MUSIC SALES LIMITED, NEWMARKET ROAD, BURY ST. EDMUNDS, SUFFOLK IP33 3YB.

WWW.MUSICSALES.COM

Say It Isn't So

Words & Music by Jon Bon Jovi & Billy Falcon

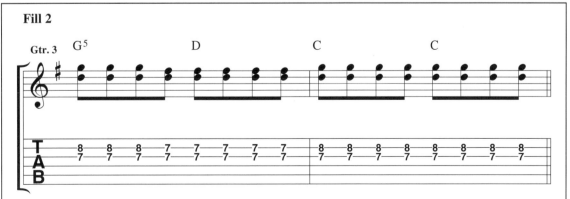

It's My Life

Words & Music by Jon Bon Jovi, Richie Sambora & Max Martin

did it my way,— I just wan-na live when I'm_____ a - live._____

Solo

It's my life._____

Bridge

Ba - by stand tall when they're call-ing you out___ don't bend don't_ break, ba - by don't back down.

Thank You For Loving Me

Words & Music by Jon Bon Jovi & Richie Sambora

Chorus

Gtr. 1 (2º)

cont. sim.

you_____ for lov - ing me, for be-ing my eyes when

Gtr. 3 (elec.)

Gtr. 3: w/clean tone
Gtr. 4: w/Fill 2 *(2º only)*
Gtr. 2: tacet

I could-n't see._____ For part-ing my_____ lips_____ when I could-n't breathe._____ Thank

1.

you_____ for lov - ing_____ me,_____ thank you_____ for lov - ing_____ me._____ 2. I

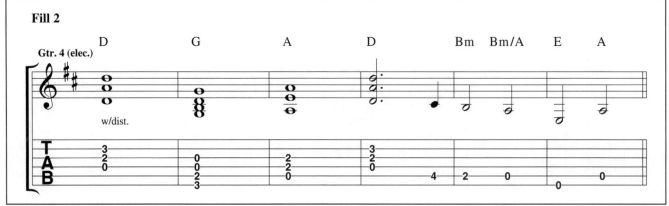

Fill 2

Gtr. 4 (elec.)

w/dist.

you___ for lov - ing___ me.

You pick me up when I fall down,___

you ring the bell be - fore they count me out.___

If I was drown-ing you would part the sea,

and risk your___ life to res - cue me,___ yeah,

yeah, yeah, yeah, yeah, yeah,___ yeah.

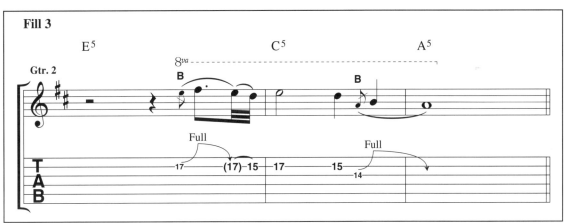

Fill 3

Two Story Town

Words & Music by Jon Bon Jovi, Richie Sambora, Mark Hudson & Dean Grakal

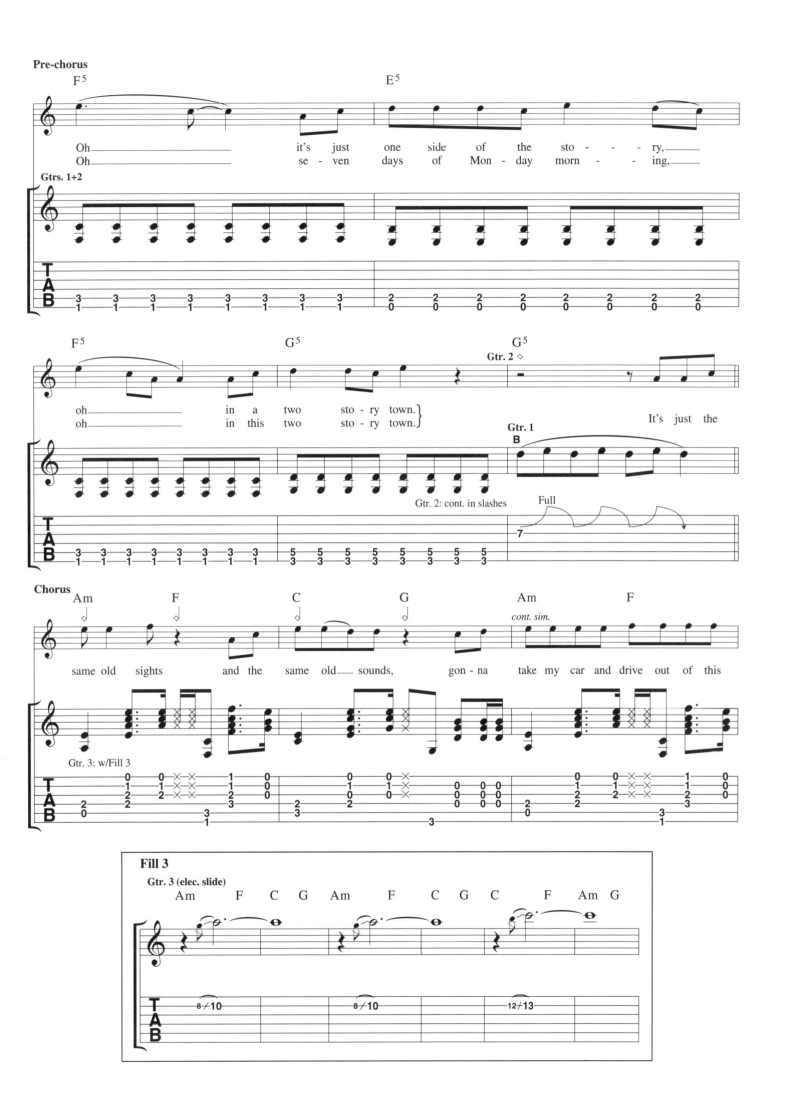

Next 100 Years

Words & Music by Jon Bon Jovi & Richie Sambora

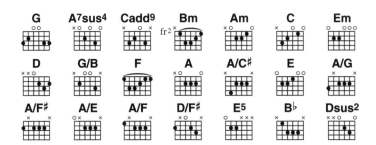

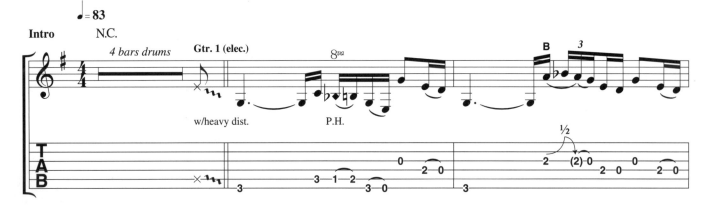

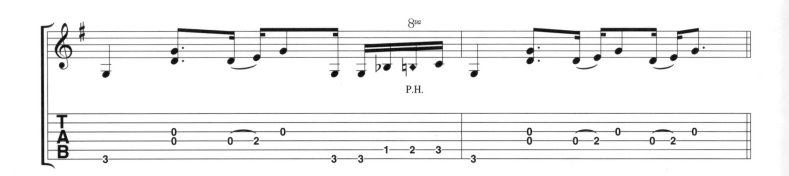

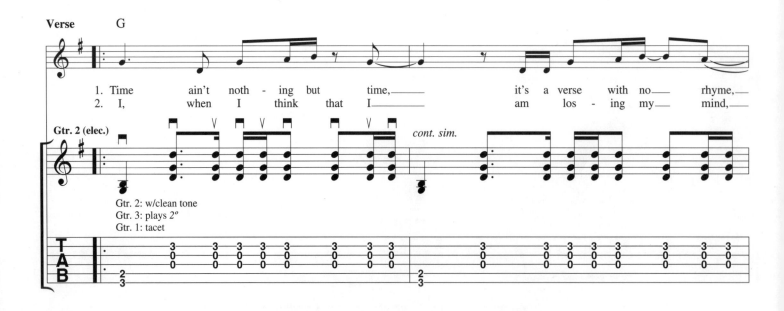

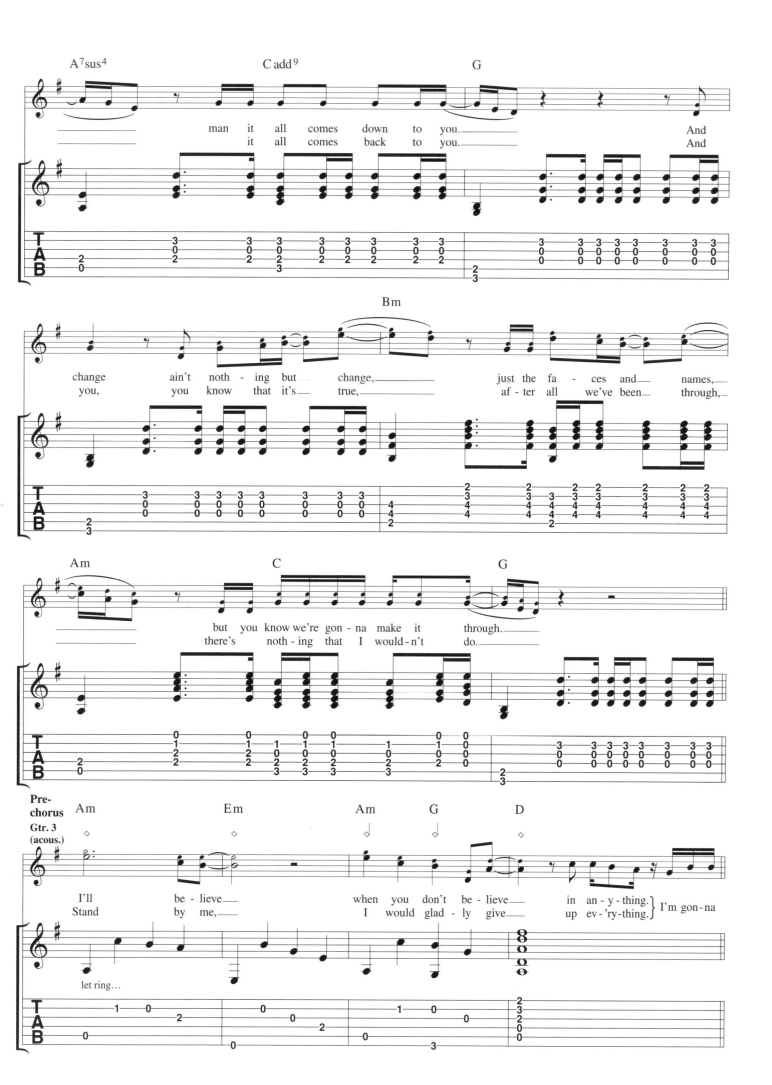

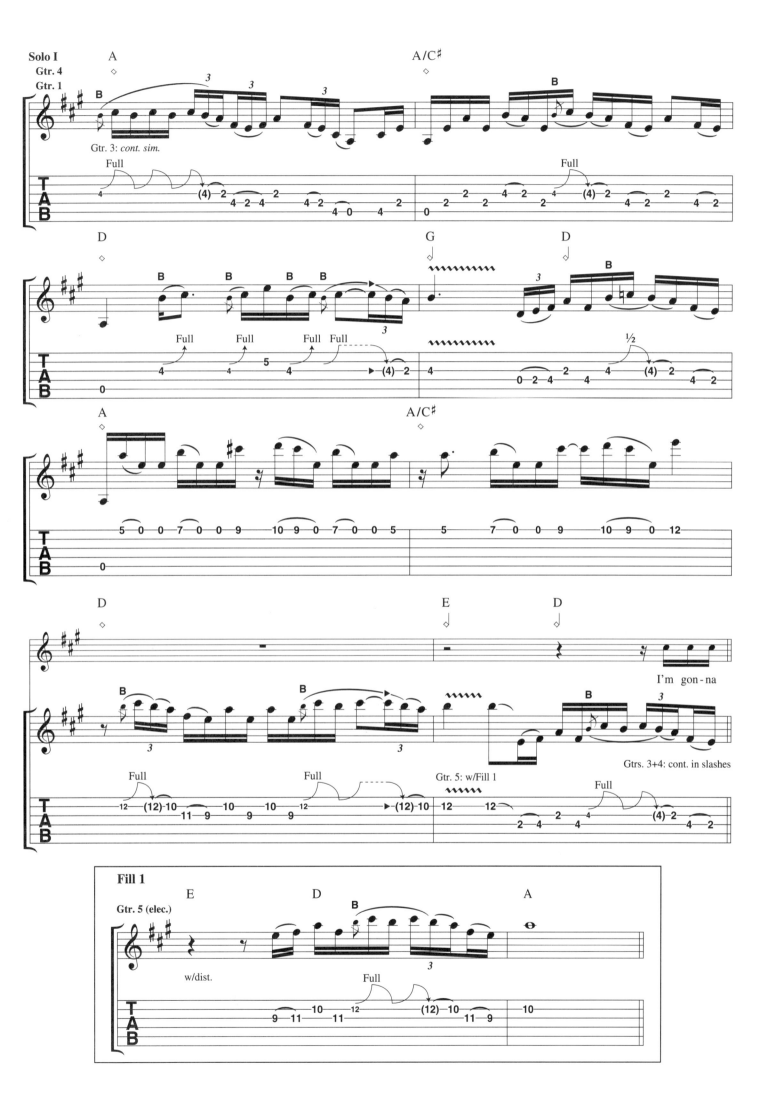

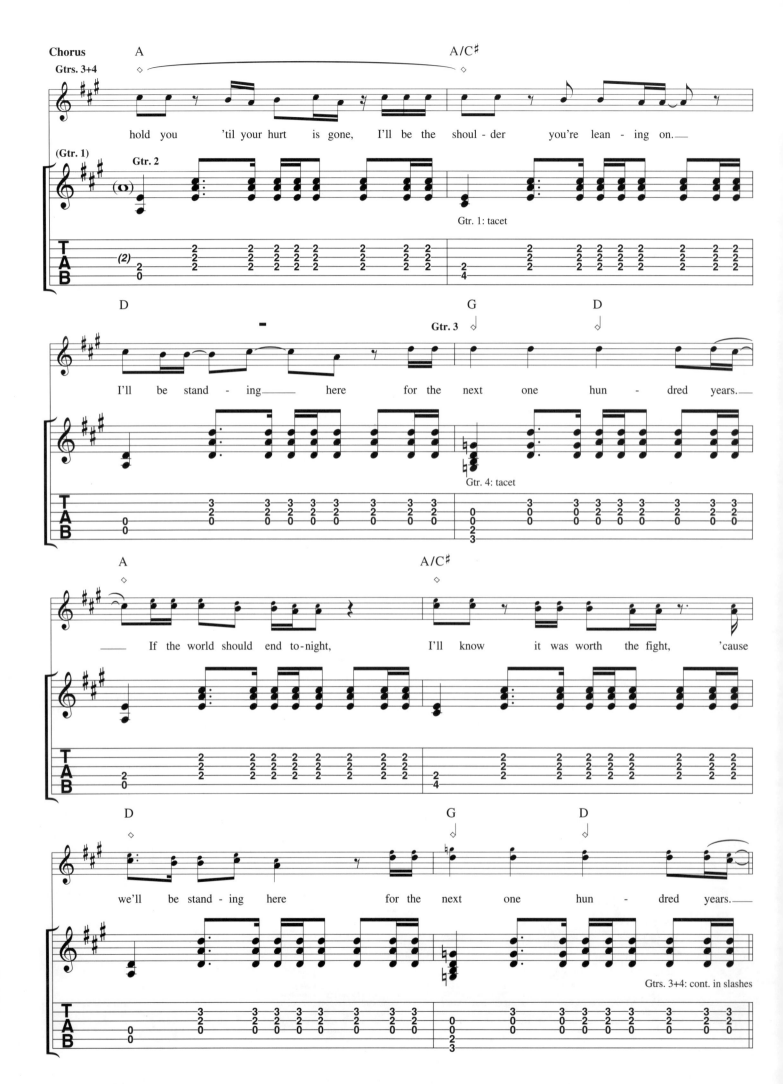

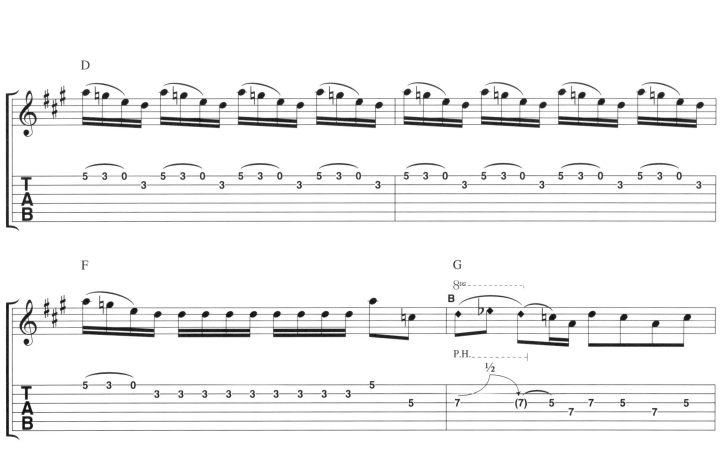

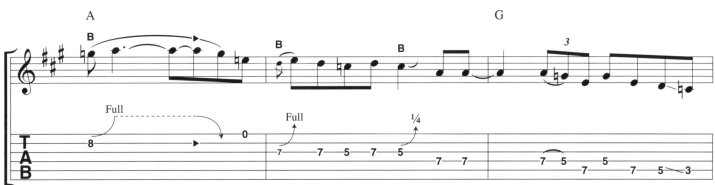

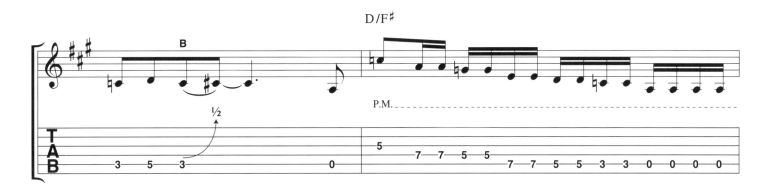

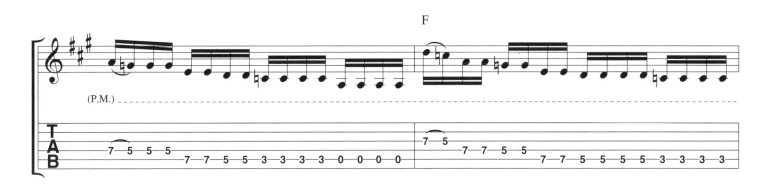

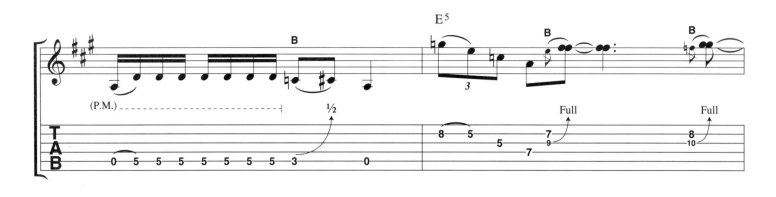
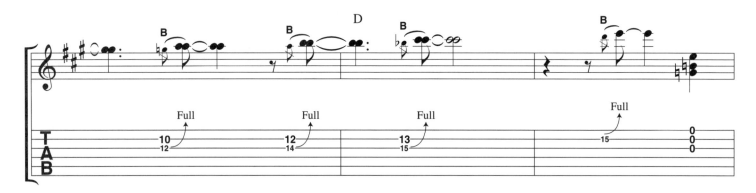
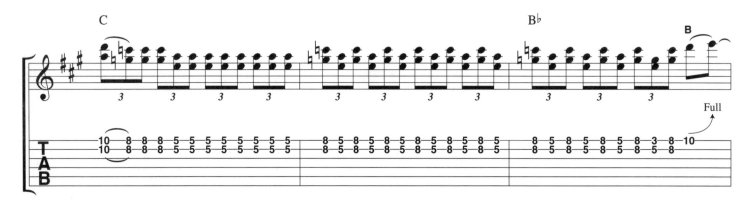
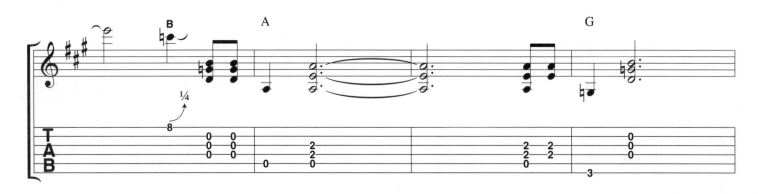
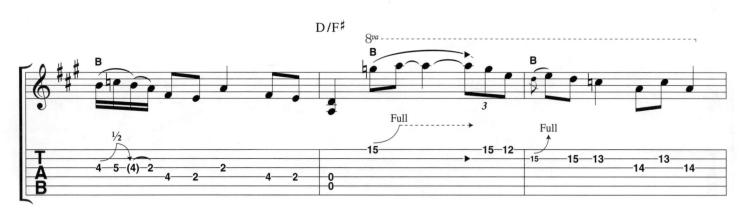

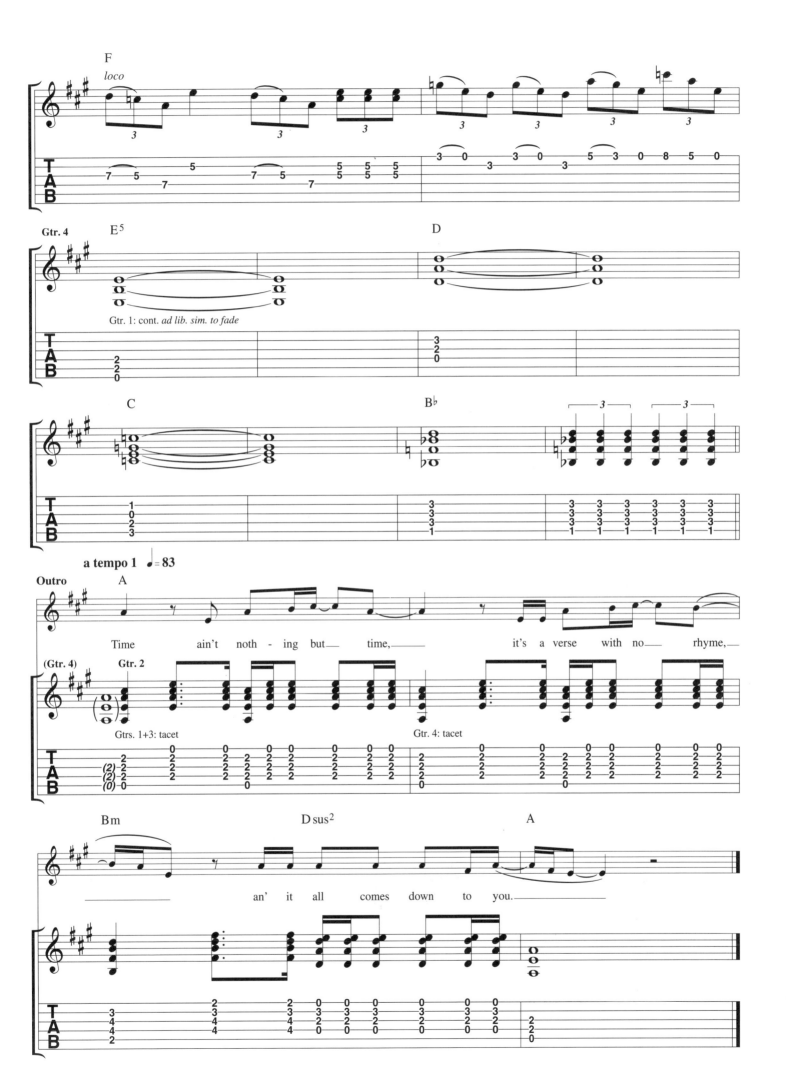

Just Older

Words & Music by Jon Bon Jovi & Billy Falcon

lit - tle wild__ a lit - tle green,__ been up and down__ an' in - be - tween, Af - ter
see your face__ you ain't no worse for wear breathe in __ that Ca - li - for - nia air. When we

all these years__ and miles of__ me - mo - ries,__ I'm still chas - ing
took on the__ world we were__ young and brave,__ we got secrets that we'll take

dreams, but I ain't look - ing ov - er my shoul - der.⎱
to the grave, stand - ing here shoul - der to shoul - der.⎰ I

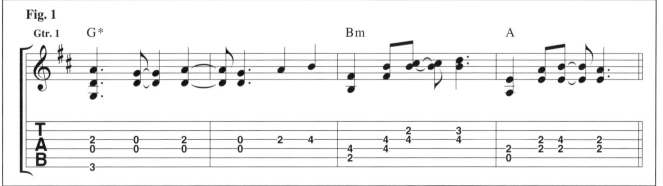

Fig. 1

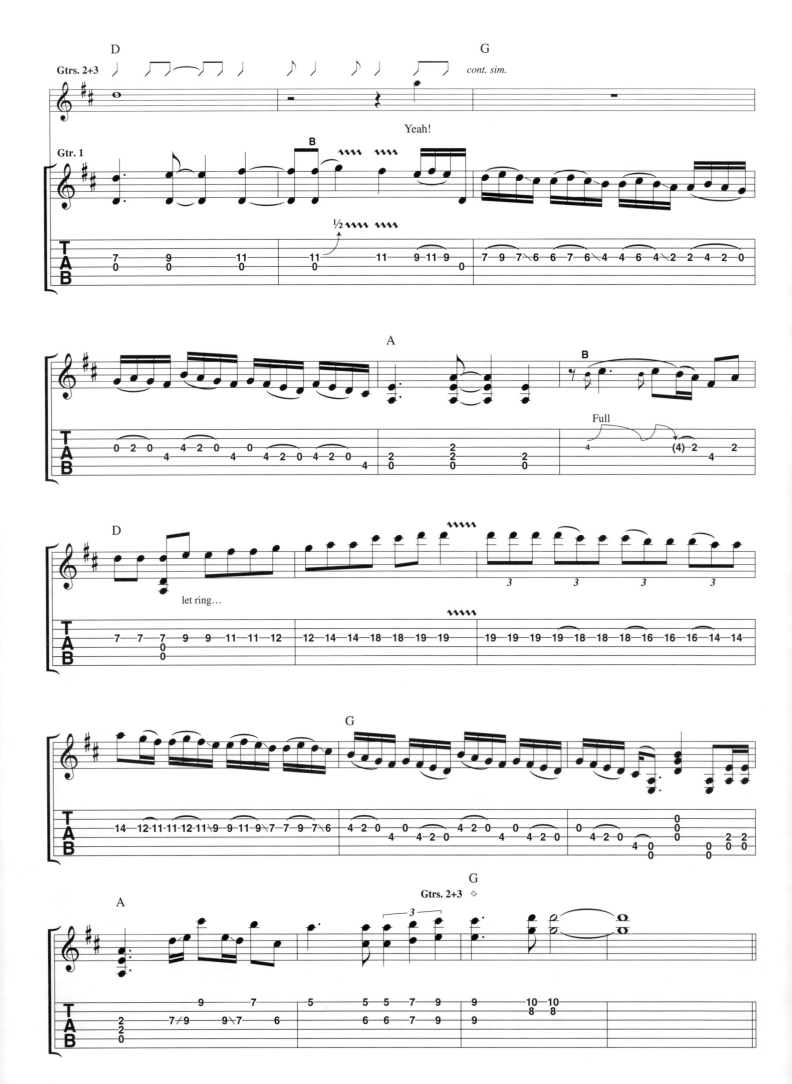

49

Mystery Train

Words & Music by Jon Bon Jovi & Billy Falcon

Save The World

Words & Music by Jon Bon Jovi

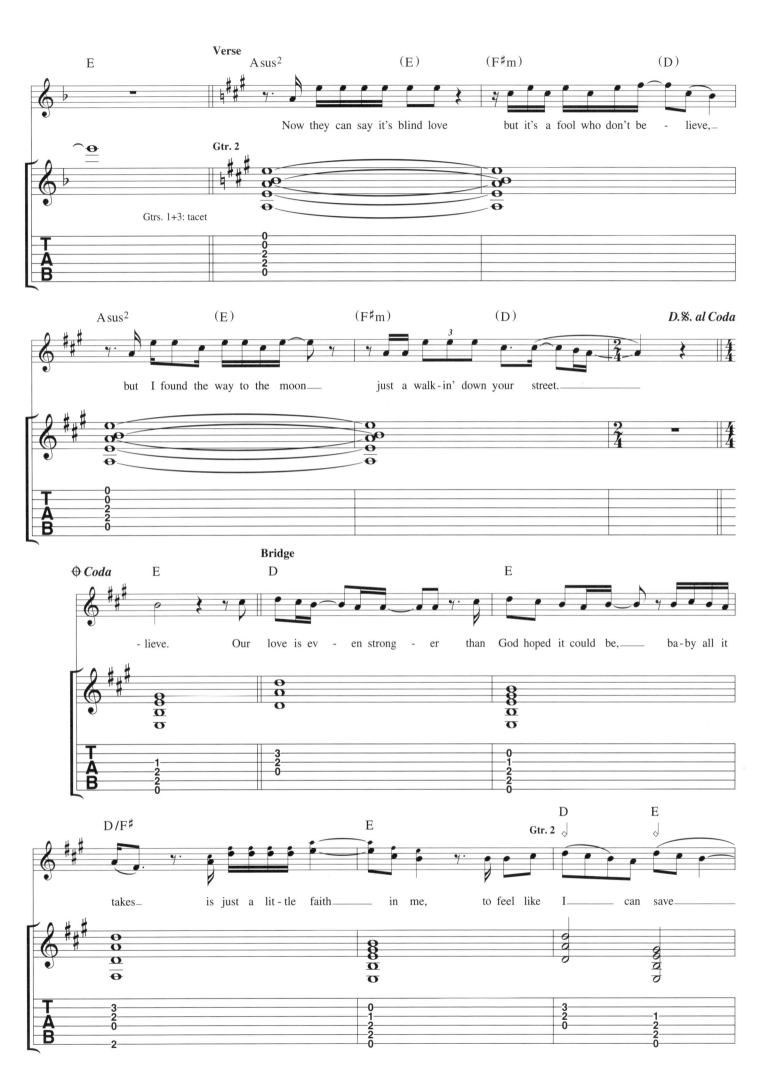

Captain Crash & The Beauty Queen From Mars

Words & Music by Jon Bon Jovi & Richie Sambora

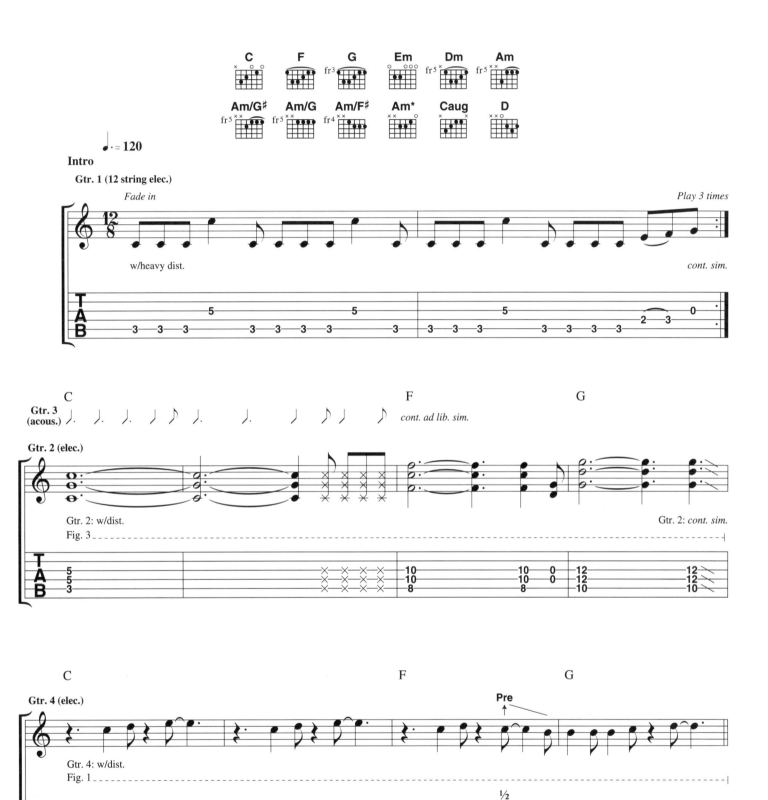

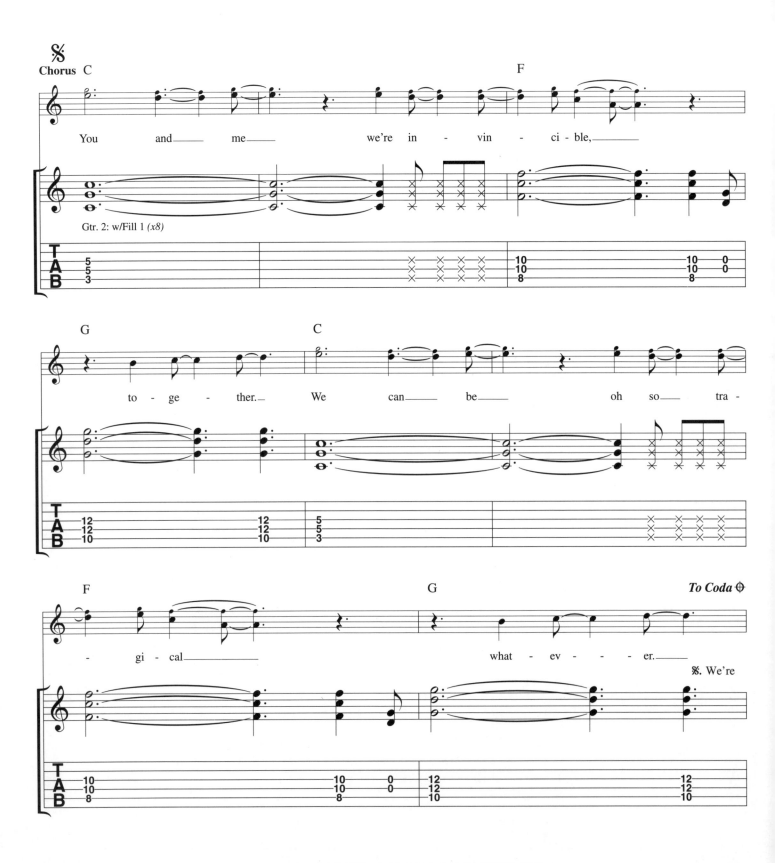

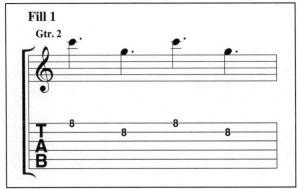

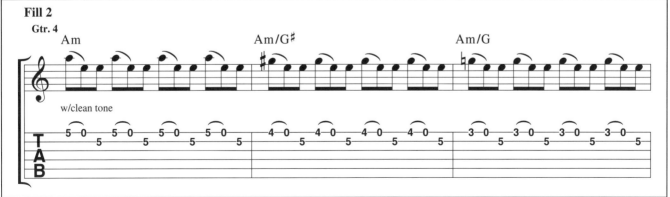

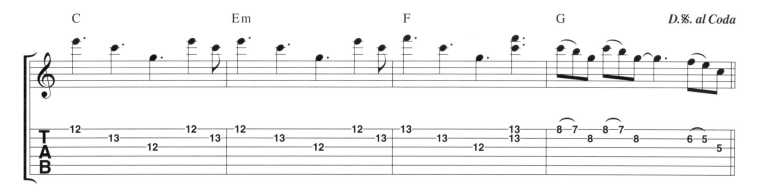

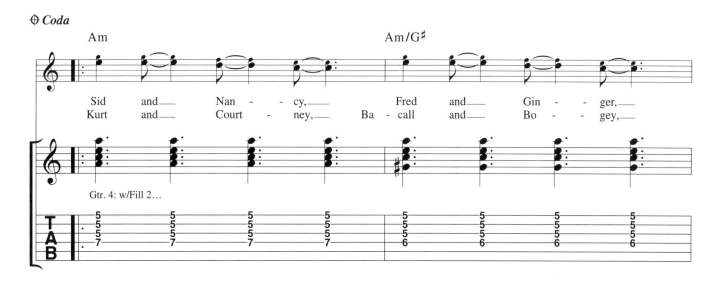

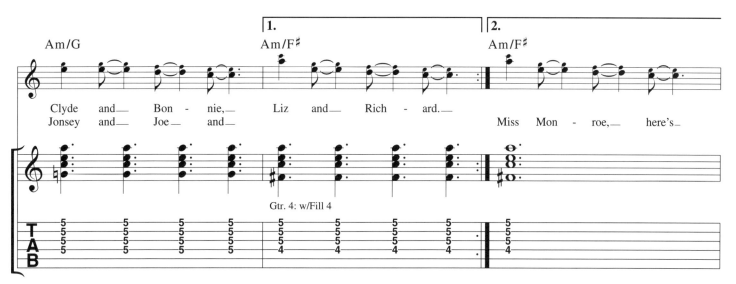

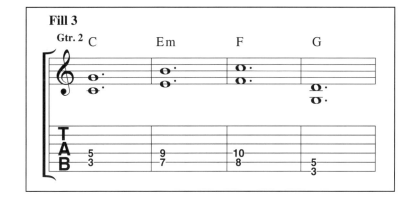

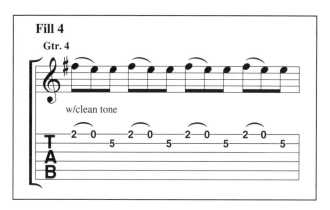

She's A Mystery

Words & Music by Jon Bon Jovi, Greg Wells & Peter Stuart

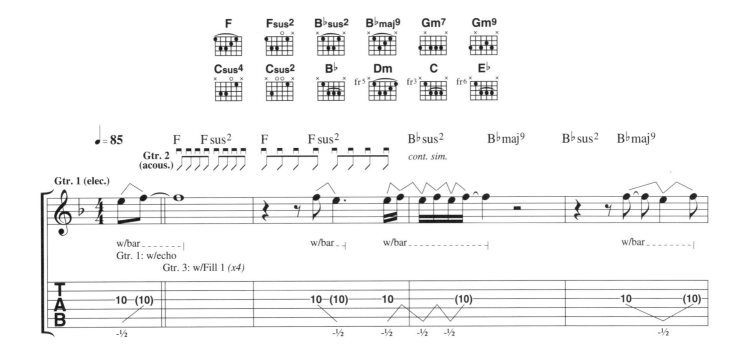

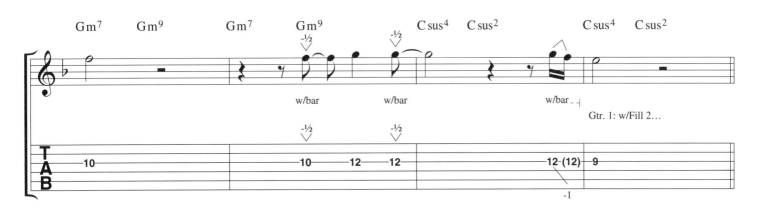

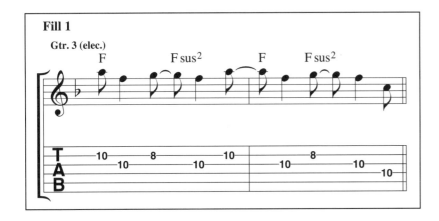

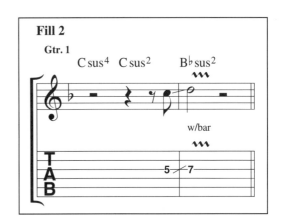

I Got The Girl

Words & Music by Jon Bon Jovi

sis - ter band - aid knees,___ won't you please___ pray for the ones___ like___ me.___ Yeah!

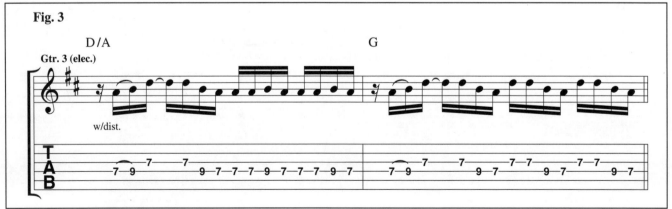

Fig. 3

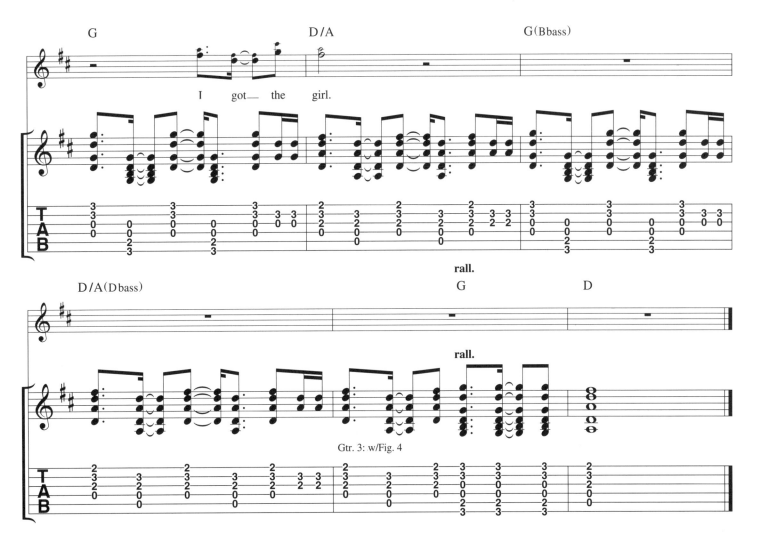

Verse 4:
Now the truth is, some day, somebody
Is gonna take her from me
But the queen of hearts will always be
A five year old princess to me
To me.

I got the girl *etc.*

I Could Make A Living Out Of Lovin' You

Words & Music by Jon Bon Jovi, Richie Sambora & Billy Falcon

One Wild Night

Words & Music by Jon Bon Jovi, Richie Sambora & Desmond Child